Play Piano with...
Muse

Published by
Wise Publications
8/9 Frith Street, London W1D 3JB, England.

Exclusive Distributors:
Music Sales Limited
Distribution Centre, Newmarket Road, Bury St Edmunds, Suffolk IP33 3YB, England.
Music Sales Pty Limited
120 Rothschild Avenue, Rosebery, NSW 2018, Australia.

Order No. AM91984
ISBN 0-7119-4100-9

Compiled by Nick Crispin.
Music arranged by Paul Honey.
Music processed by Paul Ewers Music Design.
Cover photograph courtesy of Marc Lark/LFI.
Printed in Great Britain by Printwise (Haverhill) Limited, Haverhill, Suffolk.

CD recorded, mixed & mastered by Jonas Persson.
Piano & sequencing by Paul Honey.
Guitars by Arthur Dick.
Bass by Don Richardson.
Drums by Brett Morgan.

Wise Publications
part of The Music Sales Group

London / New York / Paris / Sydney / Copenhagen / Berlin / Madrid / Tokyo

Apocalypse Please

Words & Music by Matthew Bellamy, Chris Wolstenholme & Dominic Howard

1 bar count in

C♯
4fr
F♯m
ur - gen - cy, and pull us through,
bib - li - cal, to pull us through,
his - to - ry, and pull us through,
C♯
4fr
F♯m
C♯
4fr
and pull us through.
and pull us through.
and pull us through.
And this is the
F♯m
D/F♯
2fr
E/G♯
2fr
Eaug/G♯
2fr
end, the end, this is the end
A
5fr
C♯
4fr
A
5fr
of the world.

C♯
4fr
1.
2, 3.
2. And it's
C♯sus4
4fr
C♯
4fr
F♯m
D
2fr
C♯sus4
4fr
C♯
4fr
3
Ooh,
ooh,
F♯m
D
2fr
Bm7
ooh,
oh,

B♯
3fr
C♯
4fr
To Coda
D.S. al Coda
ooh.
3. And pro -
f
Coda
C♯5
4fr
F♯m/C♯
8va
ff
8vb
C♯5
4fr
F♯m
D5
5fr
8va
8vb
B5
C♯5
4fr
F♯5
8va
8vb

Butterflies And Hurricanes

Words & Music by Matthew Bellamy, Chris Wolstenholme & Dominic Howard

1 bar count in

Dm7
Dm6
you are, and ev - 'ry - thing
Dm(♭6)
Dm
you were,
E♭7♭9/G♯
E
your num - - ber has
A7
A7♭9
A7
A
— been called.

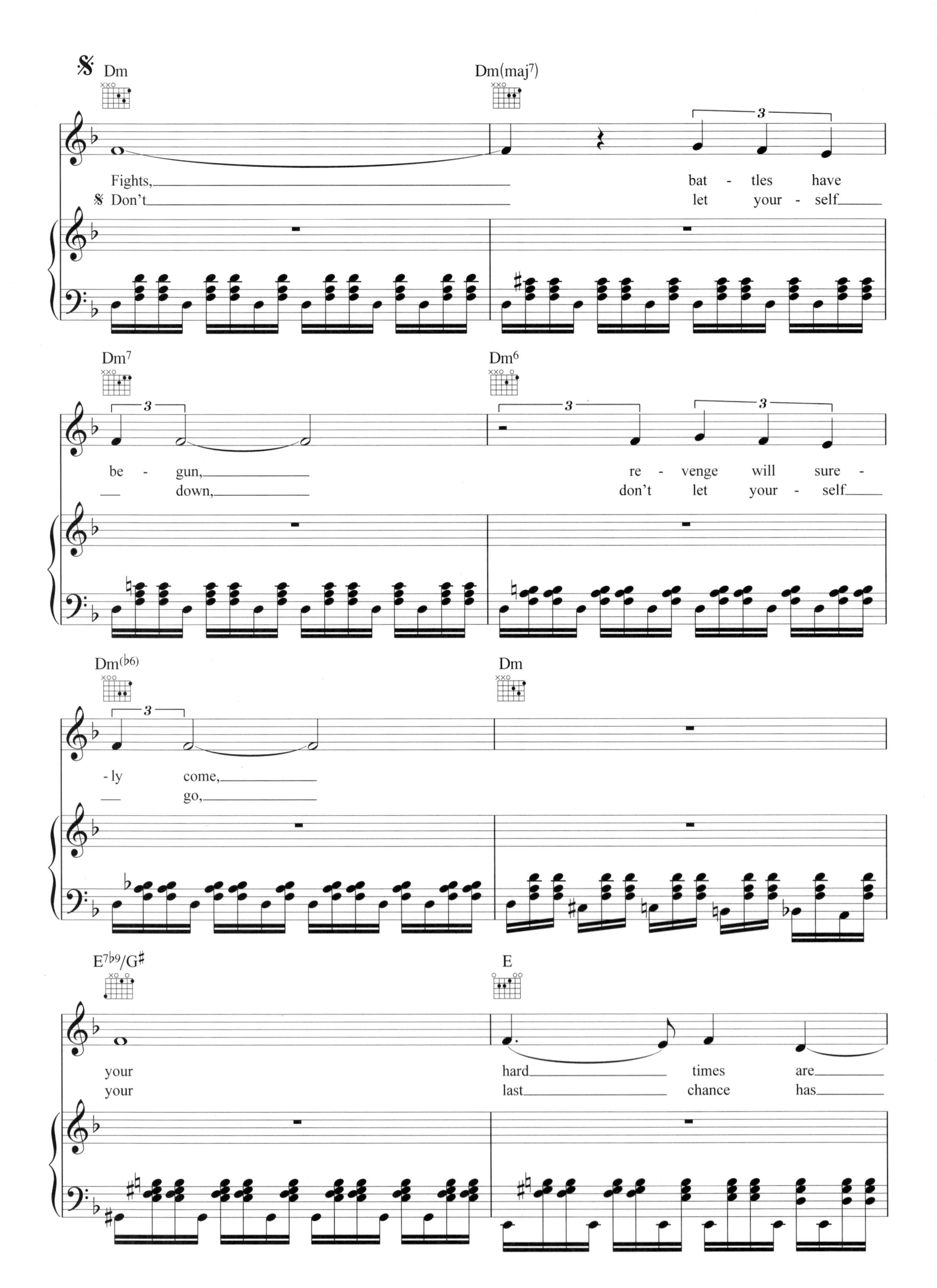
Dm
Dm(maj7)
Fights, bat - tles have
Don't let your - self
Dm7
Dm6
be - gun, re - venge will sure -
down, don't let your - self
Dm(♭6)
Dm
- ly come,
go,
E7♭9/G♯
E
your hard times are
your last chance has

A7
A7♭9
A7
A
a - head.
ar - rived.
B♭
6fr
Dm
3
Best,
you've got to be
the best,
you've got to change
B♭add9
F
the world, and use this

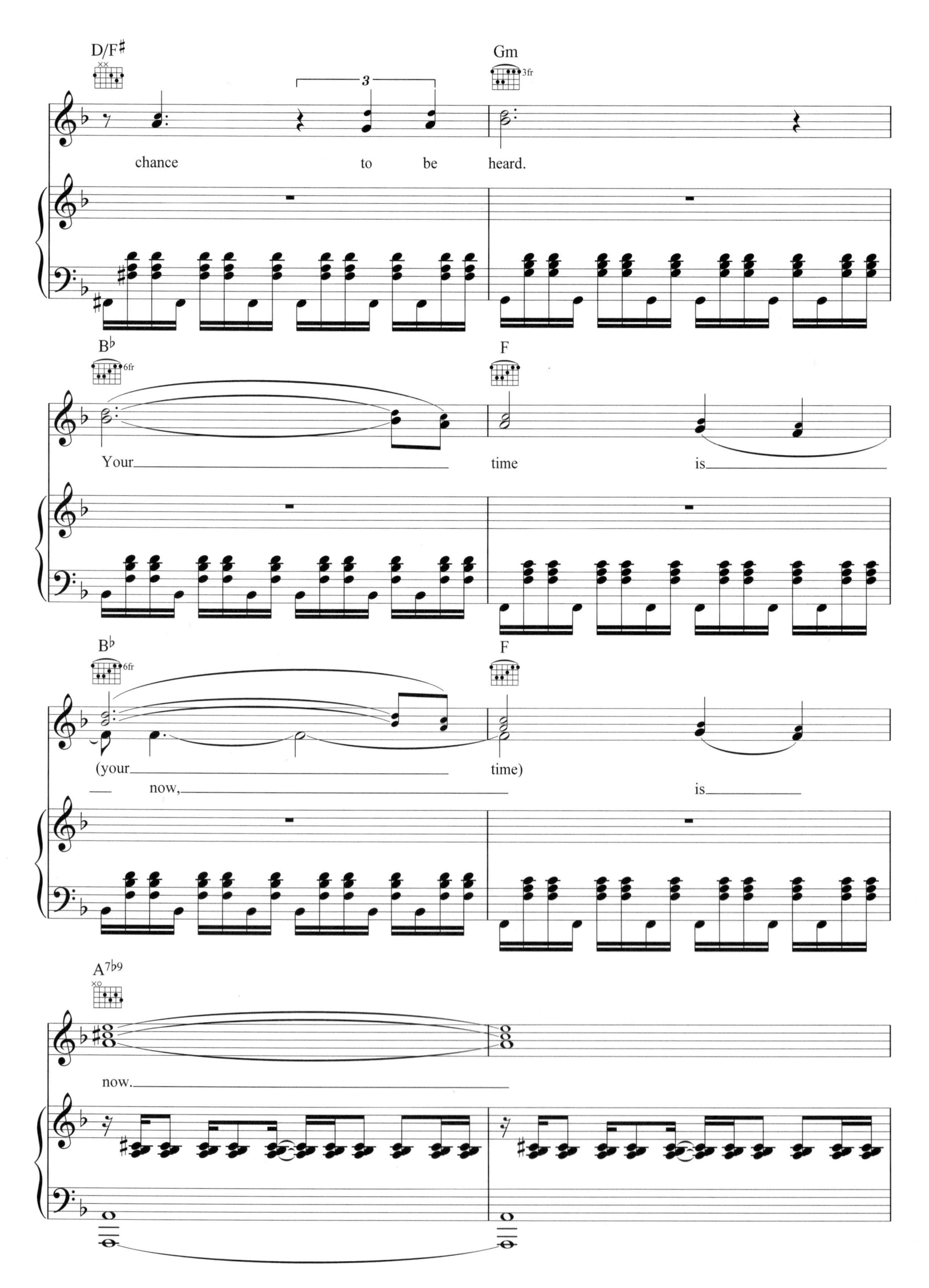
D/F♯
Gm
3fr
3
chance to be heard.
B♭
6fr
F
Your time is
B♭
6fr
F
(your time)
now, is
A7♭9
now.

1.
To Coda
ff
8vb
2.
N.C.
Strings
(8)

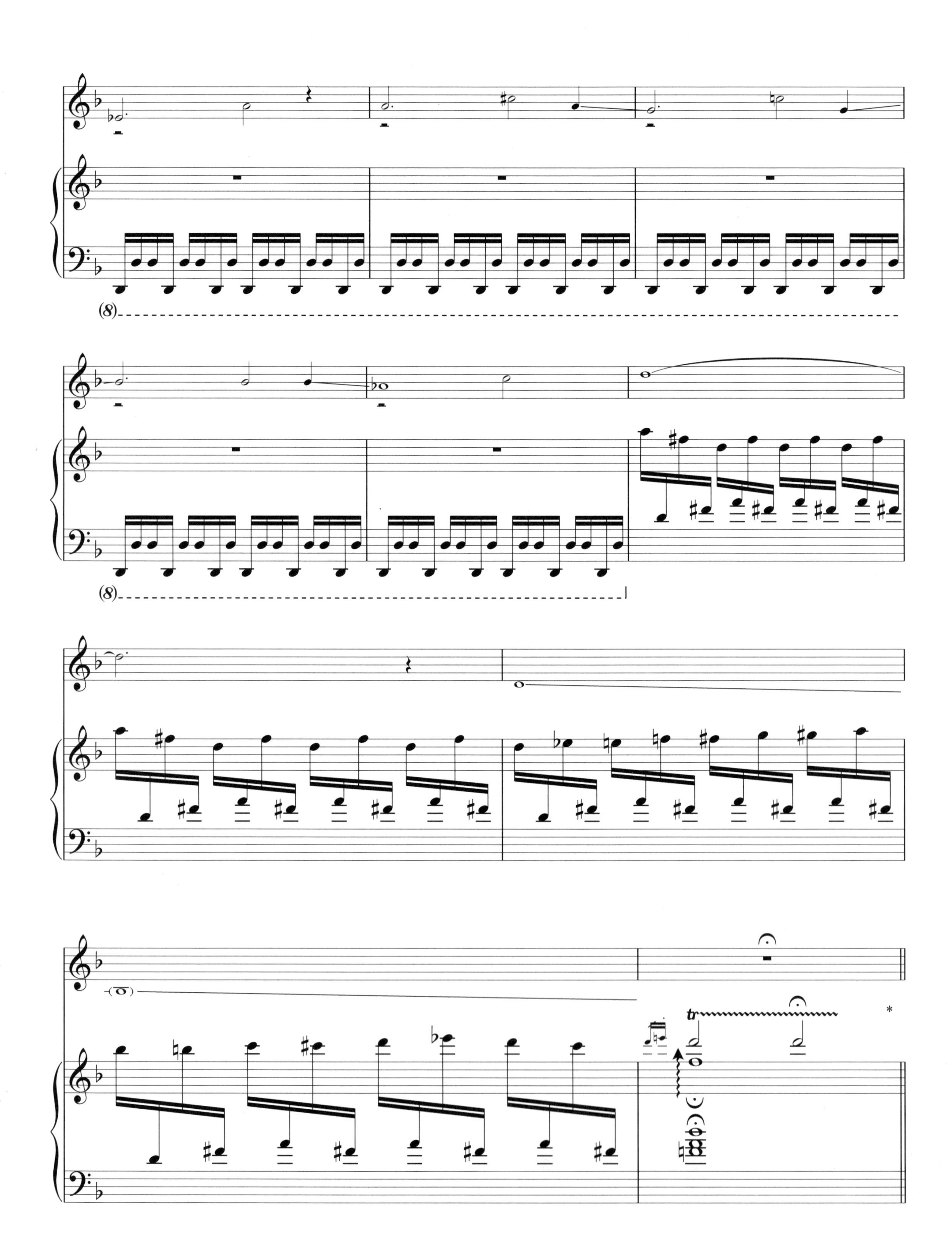
(8)
(8)
tr
*

Freely
D
2fr
5
5
5
espress.
Con pedale
Cdim7
6
6
6
5
7
3
3
5
D
2fr
5
5
5
tr
6
6

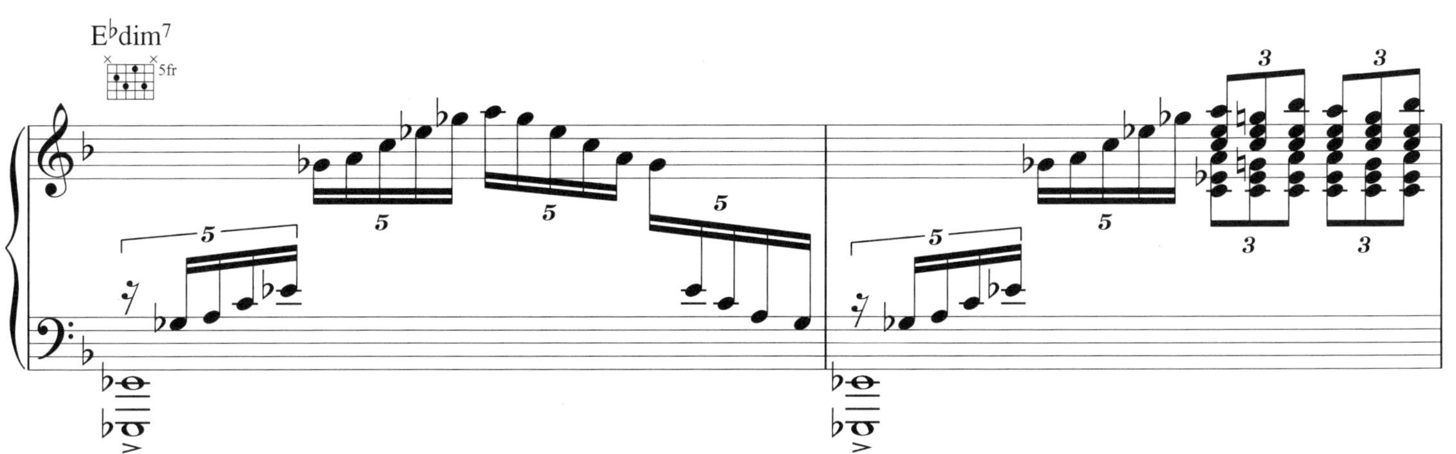

E♭dim7
5fr
5
5
5
5
5
5
3
3
3
3

D
2fr
tr
E♭dim7
5fr
N.C.
subito p
D.S. al Coda
Coda

Falling Down

Words & Music by Matthew Bellamy

2 bars count in

A
E
D/A
peop - le scream,
they were all beg - ging for your
dream.
A
A7
I'm fall - - - - ing
D/A
Dm/A
A
down,
five thou - sand hou - ses burn - ing down,
yeah,
E
D/A
A
no - one is gon - na save this
town.

F♯m
F
A
Too late, I al-rea-dy found what I was look - ing for.
Piano
mf
C♯
4fr
D
B/D♯
You know it was - n't here, no it was - n't here.
E
A
A7
8va
I was call - ing your name,
D/A
Dm/A
A
but you would ne-ver hear me sing,

E
D/A
A
you would-n't let me be - gin.
A7
D/A
So I'm crawl - - - ing a - way,
Dm/A
A
E
'cos you broke my heart in two, yeah, no I will not for - get
D/A
A
F♯m
you.
Too late, I al - rea - dy
cresc.
f

F
A
C♯
4fr
found what I was look - ing for.
You know it was -
D
B/D♯
E
- n't you, no, it was - n't you, no.
A
A7
D/A
Fall - - ing a - way,
mp
Dm/A
A
E7
you would ne - ver see me through,
no I could not for - get

D/A
A
you.
Fall -
A7
D/A
Dm/A
ing
down,
five thou - sand hou - ses
A
E7
D/A
burn - ing down,
yeah,
no - one is gon - na save this
town,
yeah.
A
F♯m
F
Too late,
I al - rea - dy found what I was look -
cresc.
f
3

A
C♯
4fr
D
B/D♯
- ing for,
no it was - n't you,
no it was -
E
A
A7
- n't you. No.
Fall - ing
mp
D/A
Dm/A
A
down,
now the world is up - side down
yeah,
rall.
E
D/A
A
I'm head - ing straight for the clouds.

Ruled By Secrecy

Words & Music by Matthew Bellamy, Chris Wolstenholme & Dominic Howard

1 bar count in

C
pres - sure and the pain.
nev - er in charge.
Fm
C(♭6)/E
4fr
Wash the blood off your hands,
Your death cre - ates suc - cess,
A♭/E♭
this time she won't un - der - stand.
re - build and
C
D♭
su - press.
Change
cresc.

B♭/D
3fr
in the air and they'll
E♭
3fr
E♭7
4fr
C7/E
hide ev - - - 'ry - where.
Fm
No one
Edim7
E♭7
To Coda
A♭
4fr
knows who's in con - trol.

A♭maj7
3fr
D
2fr
1.
Fm
2.
Fm
C/E
5fr
ff con forza

Cm/E♭
3fr
C
sim.
Fm
C/E
5fr
Cm/E♭
3fr
C
D.S. al Coda
Coda
A♭
4fr
A♭maj7
3fr
D7
con - trol.
Yeah.

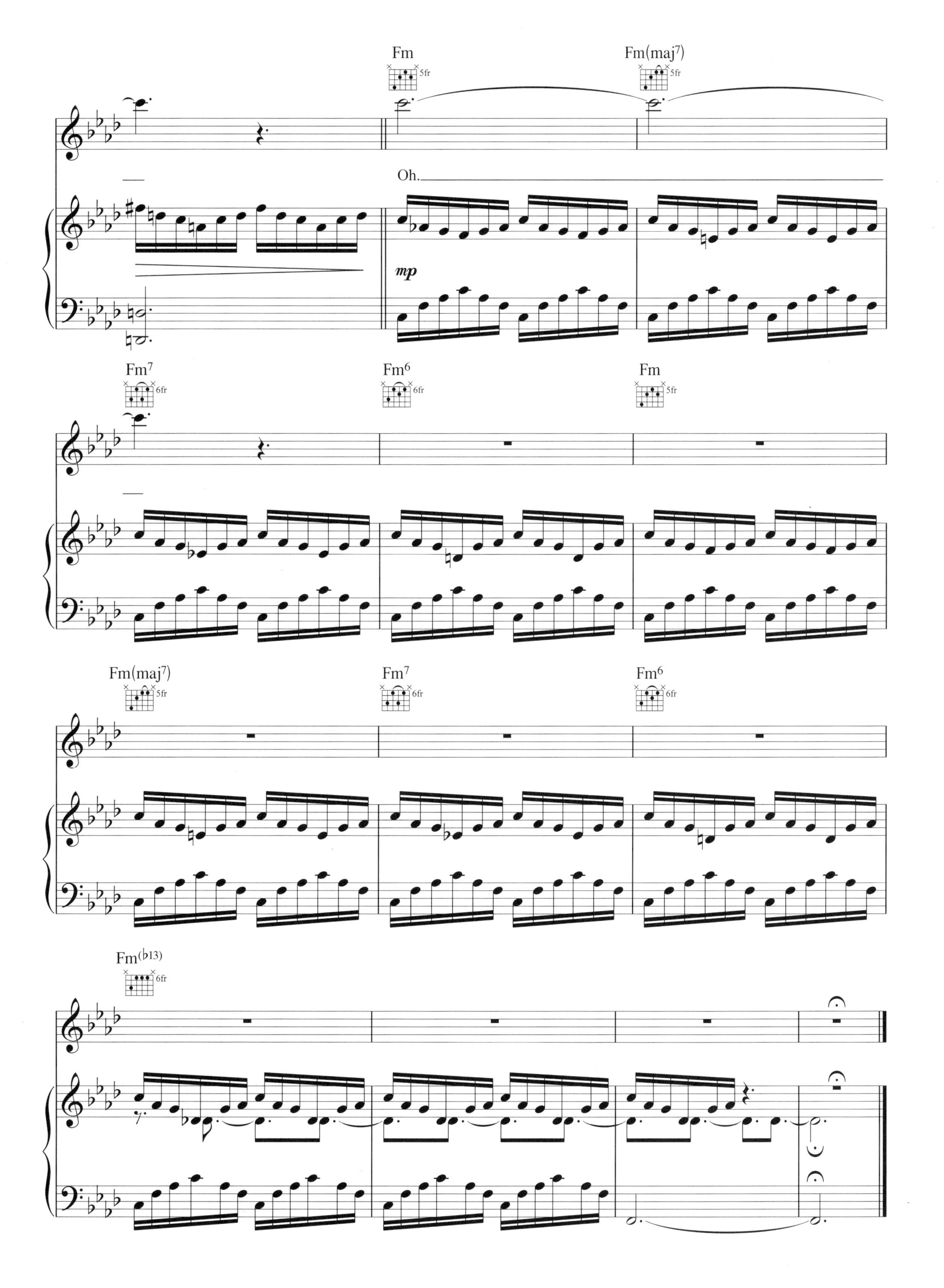
Fm
5fr
Fm(maj7)
5fr
Oh.
mp
Fm7
6fr
Fm6
6fr
Fm
5fr
Fm(maj7)
5fr
Fm7
6fr
Fm6
6fr
Fm(♭13)
6fr

Sing For Absolution

Words & Music by Matthew Bellamy, Chris Wolstenholme & Dominic Howard

E
4fr
A7
5fr
on - ly dream of you my beau - ti -ful.
Dm
5fr
B♭
6fr
Dm
5fr
B♭
6fr
Tip - toe to your room, a star - light in the gloom, I
E
4fr
A7
5fr
on - ly dream of you, and you ne - ver knew.
C
Gm
Sing for ab - so - lu - - - tion, I will
f

C
Gm
be sing-ing and fall - ing from your grace.
Ooh.
Dm
B♭
5fr
6fr
E
4fr
A7
5fr
2.There's
no -where left to hide, in no - one to con - fide, the
mf

E
4fr
A7
5fr
truth burns deep in - side and will ne-ver die.
Dm
5fr
B♭
6fr
Dm
5fr
B♭
6fr
Lips are turn - ing blue, a kiss that can't re - new, I
E7
E7♭9
E7
E7♭9
A7
A7(♯5)
A7
on - ly dream of you my beau - ti - ful.
C
Sing for ab - so -
f

Gm
-lu - - - - - - tion, I will
C
be sing - ing and fall - ing from your
Gm
grace.
Gm(add9)
3fr
Oh.
Dm
5fr
B♭
guitar solo

E
A7
5fr
C
Sing for ab - so -
Gm
- lu - - - - - - tion, I will
C
be sing - ing and fall - ing from your

Gm
Gm(add9)
3fr
grace.
Yeah.
Dm
5fr
I won't re - main un -
B♭
-rec - ti - fied,
and our souls
E
4fr
won't be ex -

Asus4
A
humed.
Dm
B♭
5fr
6fr
mf
dim.
rall.
F

Space Dementia

Words & Music by Matthew Bellamy

2 bars count in

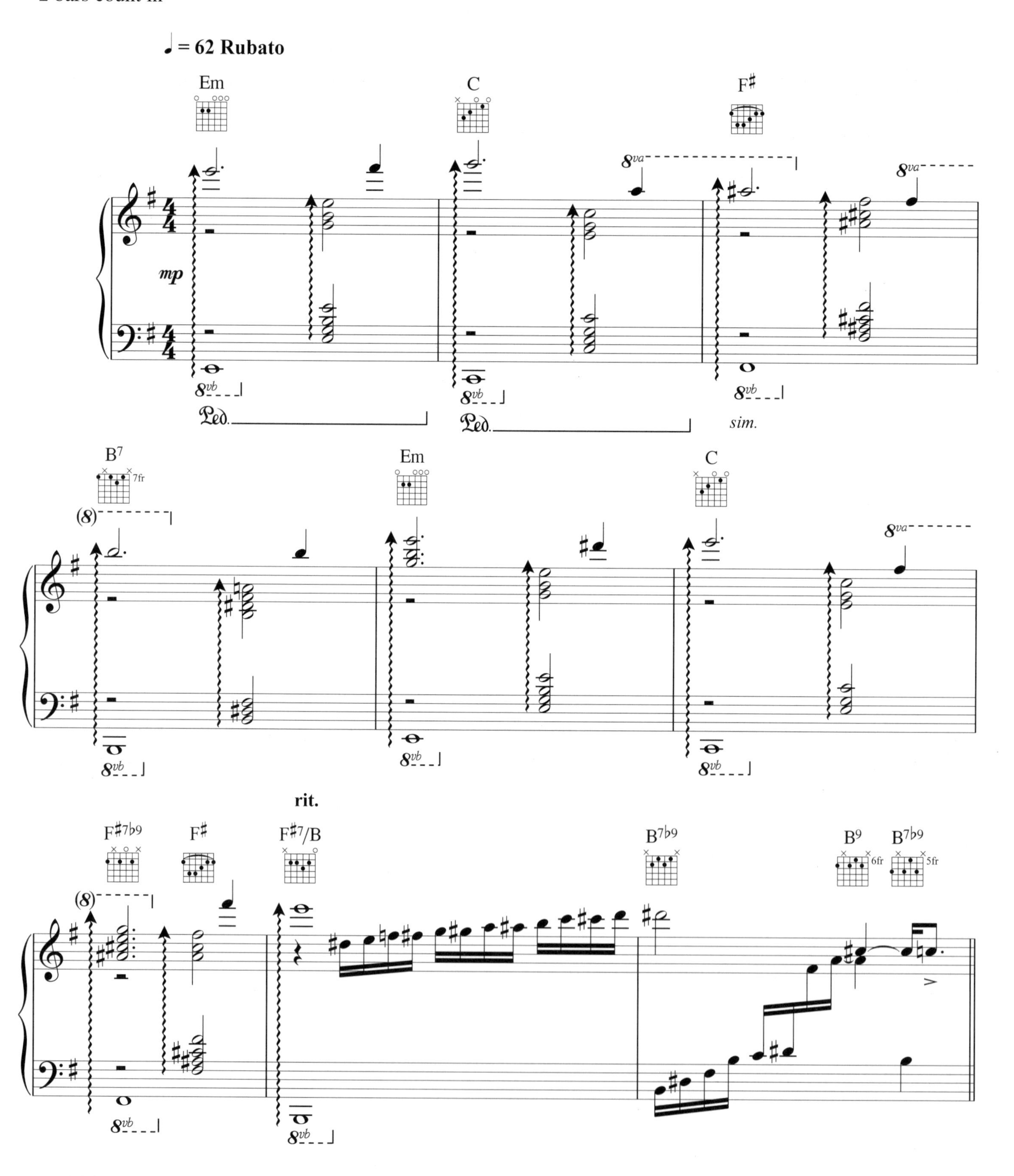

♩ = 85 a tempo
Em(add9)
7fr
L.H.
8vb
sim.
Mmm.
1. H
Em(add9)
7fr
8 is the
(2.) sick be- cause I a -
(3.) die I cut your
F♯dim
8fr
one for me, it gives me
- dore you so, I love all the
name in my heart, we'll des - troy this

G6
all I need, helps me
dir - ty tricks and twist - ed
world for you, I know you
8vb
Am(add9)
co - ex - ist with the chill.
games you play on me.
want me to feel your
Bm7
F#7/C#
pain.

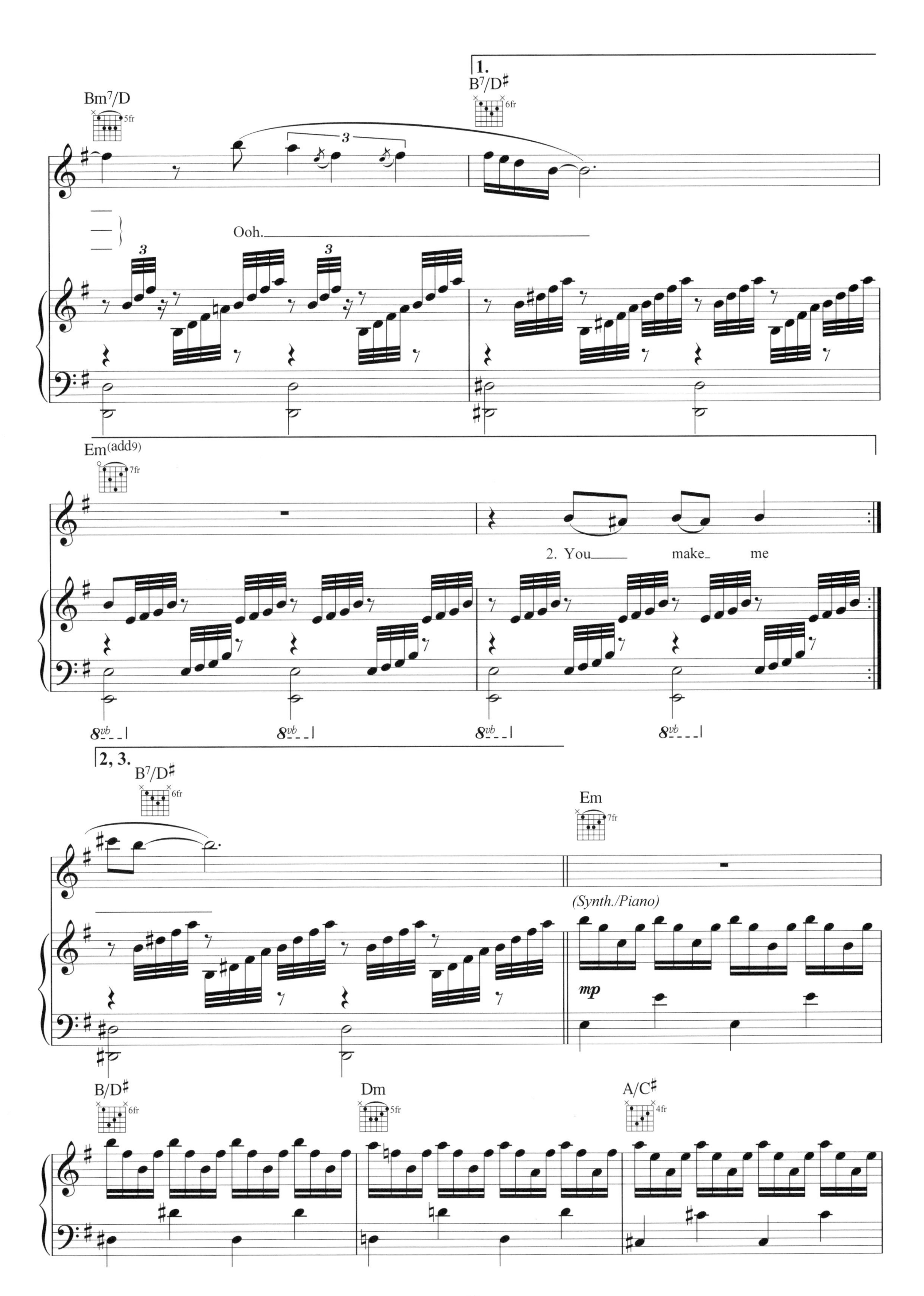
1.
Bm7/D
B7/D♯
5fr
6fr
Ooh.
Em(add9)
7fr
2. You make me
8vb
2, 3.
B7/D♯
Em
(Synth./Piano)
mp
B/D♯
Dm
A/C♯
4fr

Am/C
B7
E
Em
Space de -
A7
A6
Bm7
Dm
F♯aug
-men - tia in your eyes and
G7
F♯aug/A♯
Bm
C
peace will a - rise
F♯aug
B
Daug
and tear us a - part

E
7fr
F(♭5)
8fr
and make us mean - - ing - -
F♯7
9fr
Baug
7fr
To Coda
-less a - gain.
B7♯9
(Piano)
mf
Em(add9)
D.S. al Coda
3
Mmm.
3.You'll make us wan - na
8vb
8vb
8vb
8vb

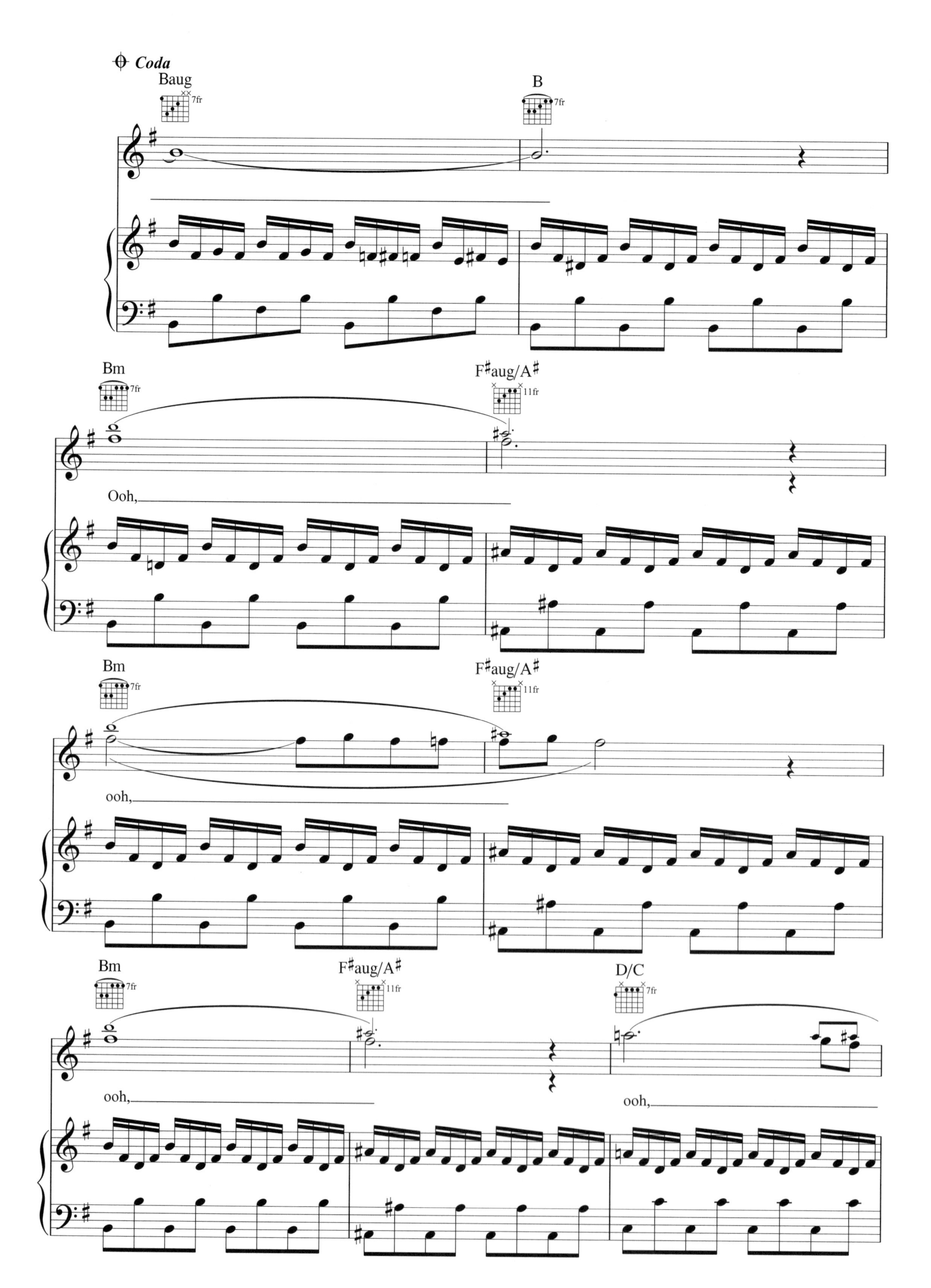
Coda
Baug
7fr
B
7fr
Bm
7fr
F♯aug/A♯
11fr
Ooh,
Bm
7fr
F♯aug/A♯
11fr
ooh,
Bm
7fr
F♯aug/A♯
11fr
D/C
7fr
ooh,
ooh,

G/B
Gm/B♭
3fr
Dsus4/A
5fr
D/A
5fr
ooh.
A7
5fr
slower
C
ff
8vb
Em
C
F♯
B
Electric guitar
(8)
Em
C
F♯
Bsus4
B
Em
(8)

Sunburn

Words & Music by Matthew Bellamy

2 bars count in

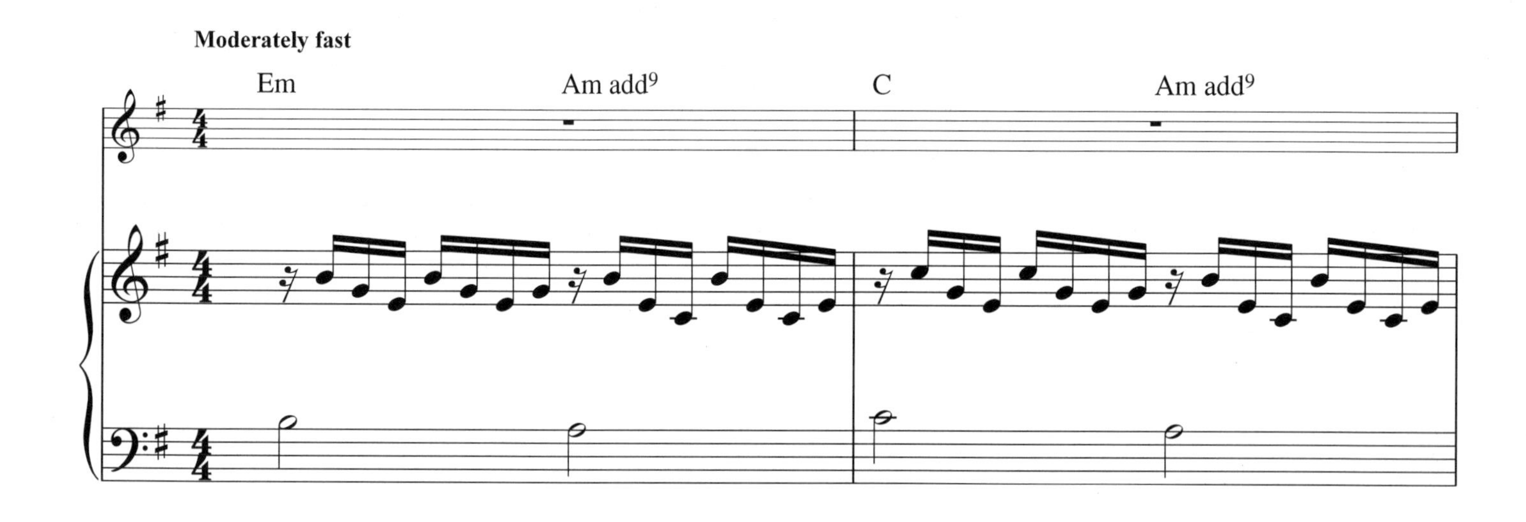

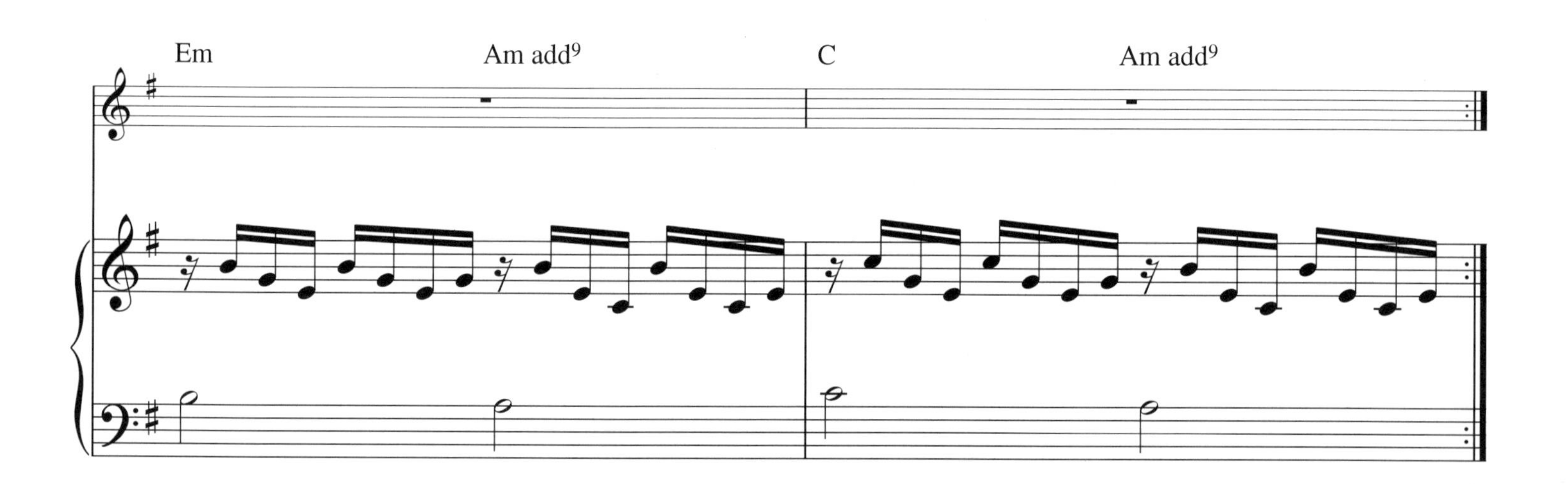

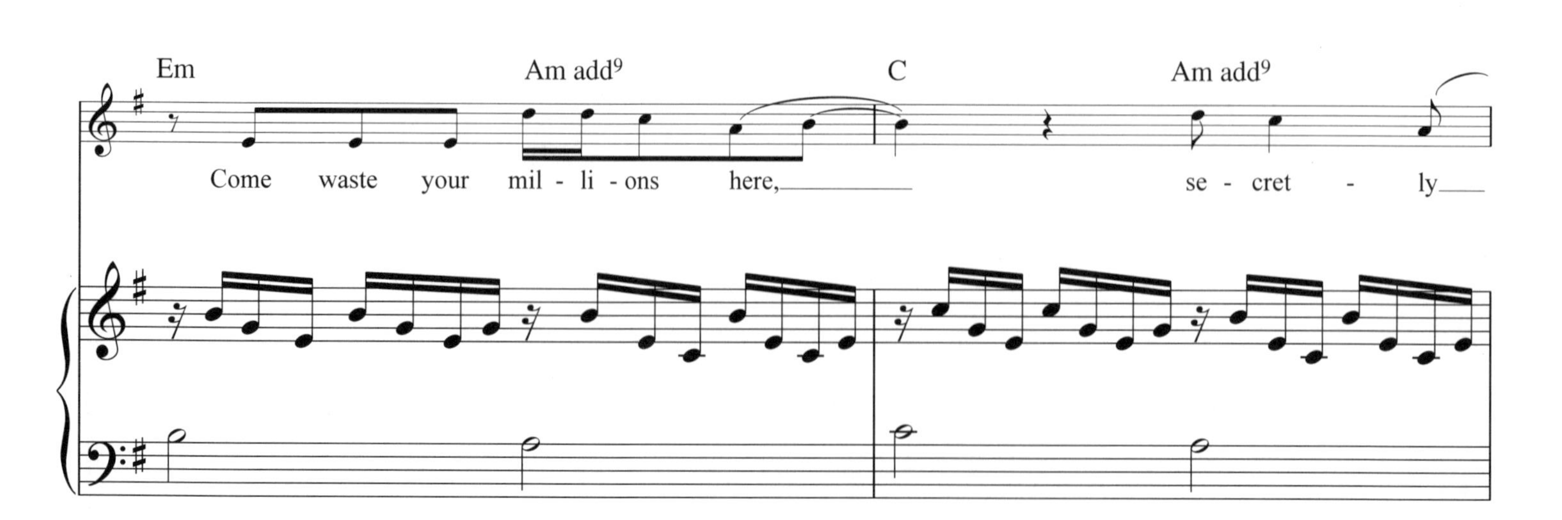

Em
Am add9
C
Am add9
she sneers.
An - oth - er cor - por - ate show;
a guilt - y con -
science grows.
2. I'll
feel
a guilt - y con -
3. Come let the truth be shared,

Em
Am add9
C
Am
- science grow
and I'll feel
no - one ev - er dared
to break
Em
Am add9
C
Am add9
a guilt - y con -
these end - less lies,
se - cret - ly
Em
Am add9
C
Am add9
- science grow.
she cries.
Am6
Am7
Em
Am6
Am7
She burns like the sun, and I can't look

Em
Am6
Am7
Em
a - way.
And she'll burn
our ho - ri - zons,
A
Am7
Em
make no mis - takes.
1.
Em
Am add9
(Guitar solo)
C
Am add9
Em
Am add9
C
Am add9
2.
N.C.
Am6 Am7
Em
Guitar solo (Piano tacet)
(8)

Am6
Am7
Em
Am6
Am7
Em
Am6
Am7
Em
Em
And I'll hide from the world
Am6
Am7
Em
be-hind a bro - - ken frame;
Am6
Am7
Em
and I'll run for-ev - er,

Am6
Am7
Em
I can't face the shame.
Am6
Am7
Em
And I'll hide from the world
Am6
Am7
Em
be - hind a bro - - ken frame
Am6
Am7
Em
and I'll run for - ev - er,

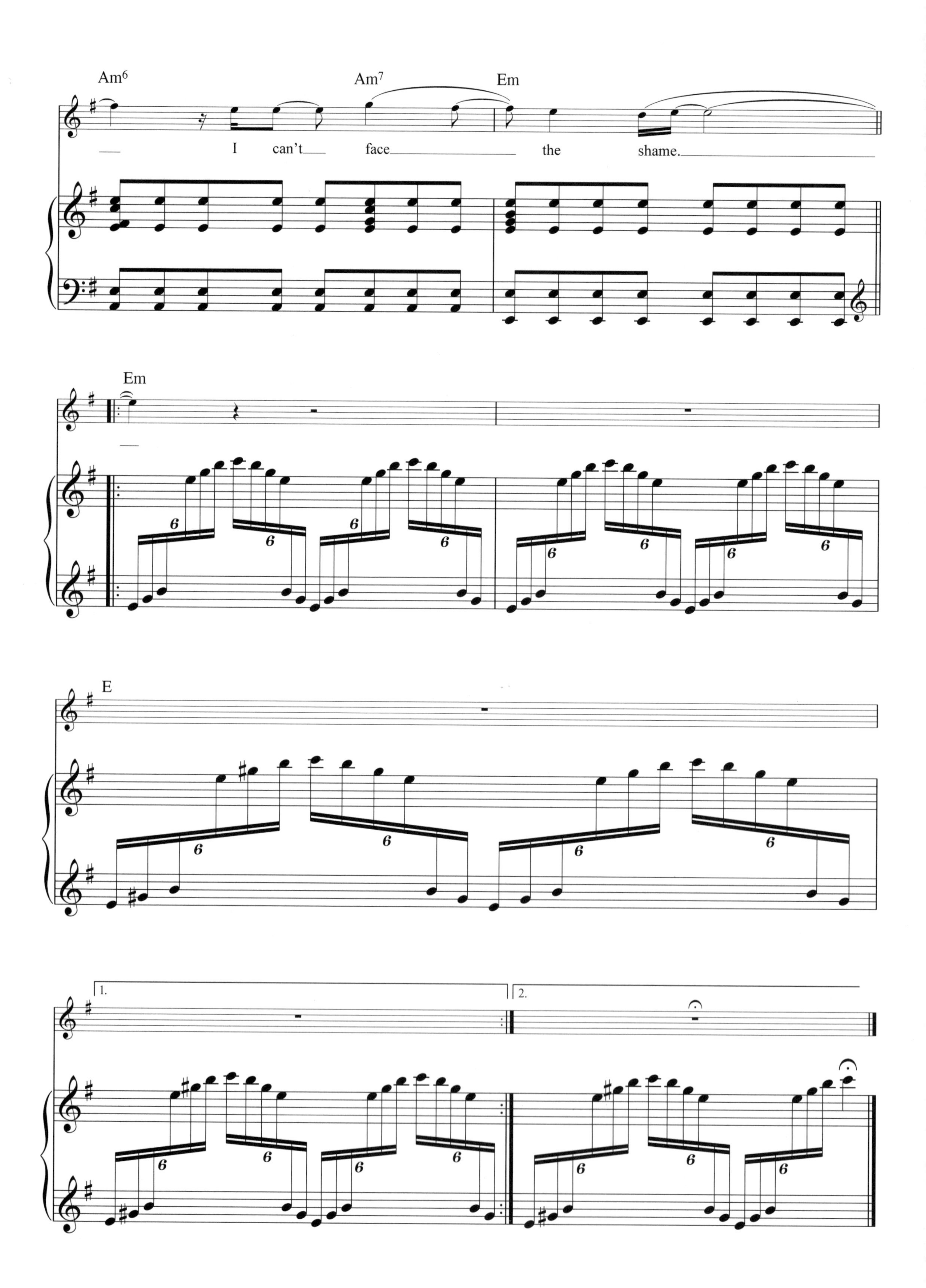
Am6
Am7
Em
I can't face the shame.
Em
E
1.
2.

Feeling Good

Words & Music by Leslie Bricusse & Anthony Newley

4 beats count in

Gm
Gm7/F
Em7♭5
E♭
drift-ing on by you know how I feel.
Blos - som in the trees you know how I feel. It's a
free - dom is mine and you know how I feel.
Gm/D
Gm/C
3fr
Gm/B♭
A7sus4
To Coda
new dawn, it's a new day, it's a new life for
C7
3fr
D7
5fr
N.C.
1.
Gm
Gm/F
and I'm feel - ing good.
Gm/E♭
Gm/D
2.
Gm/D
Gm/E♭
good.
Ped.

Gm/E
Gm/E♭
N.C.
Dra - gon - flies all out in the sun,
(Bass)
you know what I mean, don't you know.
Butter-flies are all hav-ing fun,
(Electric Piano)
you know what I mean.
Sleep in peace,
when day is done and this old world is a new world, and a bold world for

Gm
Gm/F
Gm/E♭
Gm/D
D.S. al Coda
me.
Coda
C7
3fr
A
me.
Feel-ing good
ooh,
F
E♭7
aah,
ooh,
D7
5fr
N.C.
ooh,

4 5 6 7 8 9

03/07 (61516)

CD Track Listing

Full performance demonstration tracks...

1. Apocalypse Please

(Bellamy/Wolstenholme/Howard) Taste Music Limited

2. Butterflies And Hurricanes

(Bellamy/Wolstenholme/Howard) Taste Music Limited

3. Falling Down

(Bellamy) Taste Music Limited

4. Ruled By Secrecy

(Bellamy/Wolstenholme/Howard) Taste Music Limited

5. Sing For Absolution

(Bellamy/Wolstenholme/Howard) Taste Music Limited

6. Space Dementia

(Bellamy) Taste Music Limited

7. Sunburn

(Bellamy) Taste Music Limited

8. Feeling Good

(Bricusse/Newley) Concord Music Limited

Backing tracks only (without piano)...

9. Apocalypse Please
10. Butterflies And Hurricanes
11. Falling Down
12. Ruled By Secrecy
13. Sing For Absolution
14. Space Dementia
15. Sunburn
16. Feeling Good

To remove your CD from the plastic sleeve,
lift the small lip to break the perforations.
Replace the disc after use for convenient storage.